WEDDING DATE:

_____

NAMES:

_____

_____

HELPING COUPLES CREATE GREAT MARRIAGES

BETTER TOGETHER

Design by: Jessica Amsberry

ISBN 9781635820737

FIRST EDITION

PRAYER

Loving Father,

as we prepare for marriage,

bless us with the desire and strength

to grow in our love for you and for each other.

Open our hearts to the areas of our relationship that need to change

in order for us to carry out the mission

and experience the joy you have imagined for our lives.

Grant that, as we approach our wedding day

and look toward a new life together,

we may remember what is most important

and work toward creating a strong, lasting marriage.

Give us courage when we are afraid, hope when we are discouraged,

and clarity in times of decision.

We invite you into our lives today,

and make ourselves available to you.

Help us to become the-best-version-of-ourselves by seeking your will.

May our marriage be a living example of your love in the world.

Amen.

Table of Contents

Welcome

Congratulations!

Planning your wedding is an exciting time, but it can also be pretty stressful. You have the opportunity to make your wedding a beautiful experience. That's the purpose of this journal—to help you get the details figured out so you can look forward to your big day and married life together.

This journal lays out the major aspects of the wedding planning process, along with helpful tips and resources, to help you plan an incredible wedding.

Here are four suggestions to guide your journey:

1. **Decide what is most important.** The months leading up to your wedding will be filled with meetings, budgets, checklists, and many decisions, both large and small. Decide up front what is most important to you and your fiancé. When you know what matters most and what matters least, you can make quicker and better decisions, and you will be less distracted by the smaller details.

2. **Make decisions together.** This wedding is a celebration of your union, so it is good to make choices as a couple. It will bring you closer together and provide support for each other during this stressful time.

3. **Do not fixate on perfection.** You may feel pressured to make everything just right on your wedding day. It is natural to desire perfection. But rather than get lost in the details, focus on the ultimate goal of the wedding and remember what matters most and what matters least.

4. **Pray together.** Prayer is a wonderful way to gain clarity on decisions and to find a sense of peace when things get stressful. The prayer at the beginning of this journal is a simple way to start.

This time will go fast, so enjoy it! When you remember what matters most and what matters least and work together, you can create an unforgettable wedding. Happy planning!

RESPOND

What is your dream for your wedding?

Take time to discuss with your fiancé what is most important to you for your wedding day. This will set your focus and help you make decisions throughout your wedding planning.

WORDS FROM A GROOM

As we planned our wedding, my wife-to-be and I were eager to work out the many details: colors, flowers, the ceremony, the food, our first dance at the reception, etc. We wanted to share our beliefs, our customs, and our own unique personalities. It was fun and exciting! And making these decisions together even helped us build our communication skills and learn to work together better as a team. But it also became rather overwhelming.

At one point in the planning process, a dear friend reminded us that the details were just that: details. Most of them had nothing to do with the marriage and the most important part of this special day at all. In the end, the main thing for us to focus on was that we were committing to one another for the rest of our lives, with God's help. The rest of our lives! Until death do us part.

Looking back on our wedding day, the experience was so much richer because we knew these small details were not the most important and were not the main focus. We were grateful for the graces we encountered through the sacrament and our vocation as husband and wife. Our details were used to glorify God in their own ways. We were blessed to have found each other and to know that we were going to spend the rest of our lives together, married and serving God with our talents and our love.

—Ethan

Timeline

Wedding planning can be overwhelming. And while you will certainly have ups and downs, getting organized with a good timeline up front will help you avoid unnecessary stress. Look at how much time you have, determine when you are going to accomplish each task, and keep track of them throughout the planning process.

The timeline on the next page is a rough guide based on popular tasks and timetables. If your engagement is longer or shorter, no worries. Simply prioritize the tasks that apply to you, and complete them chronologically as you approach your wedding date.

Keep in mind that many of these to-dos are optional, and you are welcome to add other tasks to your list as needed. **Remember to make decisions based on what is most important to you and your fiancé.** What may be important to one couple may not be necessary for you, even if it is a popular wedding tradition.

> **TIP**: Specific requirements for arranging the ceremony, enrolling in marriage preparation and NFP courses, and securing your marriage license, etc., will vary by diocese and state. Be sure to connect with your parish and do your research well in advance to ensure you are not trying to squeeze things in last-minute.

- ☐ Establish your budget (see page 14)
- ☐ Choose a wedding date and book the church for the ceremony
- ☐ Book your reception venue
- ☐ Meet with the priest or deacon who will officiate the wedding to enroll in marriage preparation courses
- ☐ Meet with the parish's point of contact for weddings
- ☐ Choose your caterer
- ☐ Select the members of your wedding party and the person or people who will assist you in the ceremony (see page 19)
- ☐ Brainstorm a guest list (see page 21)
- ☐ Choose colors and/or themes (see page 23)
- ☐ Order save-the-dates and postage (see page 25)
- ☐ Research photographers and have engagement photos taken
- ☐ Celebrate with an engagement party (see page 29)

Notes:

6-9 MONTHS
BEFORE THE WEDDING

- ☐ Decide which form of celebrating the Rite of Marriage you will be using (see page 36)
- ☐ Choose and order your wedding dress, veil, and accessories (see page 39)
- ☐ Select flowers and decor (see page 54)
- ☐ Choose and order the bridesmaids' dresses
- ☐ Book your florist, videographer, reception band or DJ, cake baker, and bartender
- ☐ Book a wedding coordinator or day-of coordinator
- ☐ Build a gift registry and wedding website (see page 65)
- ☐ Finalize your guest list
- ☐ Send save-the-dates
- ☐ Order invitations
- ☐ Book hotels for out-of-town guests and for your wedding night

Notes:

4–5 MONTHS
BEFORE THE WEDDING

☐ Buy or rent groom and groomsmen attire
☐ Book transportation for the day of the wedding (see page 68)
☐ Make honeymoon reservations
☐ Book makeup and hairstylist

Notes:

2-3 MONTHS
BEFORE THE WEDDING

- ☐ Send invitations
- ☐ Attend tastings and decide on menus for catering
- ☐ Attend tastings and order wedding cake
- ☐ Prepare ceremony programs
- ☐ Purchase wedding rings and have them fitted
- ☐ Have bridal and bridesmaid dress fittings
- ☐ Attend bridal shower and any other pre-wedding parties
- ☐ Send thank-you notes for pre-wedding party gifts
- ☐ Choose and order wedding favors
- ☐ Research marriage license requirements (see page 86)
- ☐ Draft a music list for your band or DJ (see page 82)
- ☐ Draft a list of desired photos for the photographer

Notes:

1 MONTH
BEFORE THE WEDDING

- ☐ Meet with vendors (caterer, photographer, baker, florist, etc.) to verify details
- ☐ Finalize and confirm all bookings with vendors and hotels
- ☐ Apply for your marriage license
- ☐ Give the band or DJ your finalized song list
- ☐ Give the photographer your finalized photo list
- ☐ Follow up with any guests who have not RSVP'd
- ☐ Purchase any gifts for each other, the wedding party, and parents
- ☐ Final dress fitting
- ☐ Do a trial run with hair and makeup
- ☐ Break in wedding shoes

Notes:

1-2 WEEKS
BEFORE THE WEDDING

- [ ] Pick up wedding dress, groom's suit or tux, and any other attire
- [ ] Finalize guest seating chart
- [ ] Give final head count to caterer
- [ ] Pack for honeymoon

Notes:

1-3 DAYS
BEFORE THE WEDDING

- ☐ Confirm with all vendors, hotels, officiant, and individuals assisting with the ceremony or reception
- ☐ Ensure setup and teardown are arranged for the day of the wedding
- ☐ Confirm delivery times for flowers, decorations, and catering
- ☐ Have wedding rehearsal and rehearsal dinner
- ☐ Pack all necessary items for the day of the wedding

AFTER THE WEDDING

- ☐ Submit name change to all necessary parties
- ☐ Send thank-you cards
- ☐ Have wedding dress cleaned and preserved

Notes:

Decide what is
most important.

Budget

Establishing your budget is one of the most important steps in the wedding-planning process. It will inform your decision making and help you stay on track financially. Take time to sit down together early on and figure out how much you plan to spend.

This is a breakdown of major costs. It shows what percentage of the total budget is typically spent within each category. This breakdown represents average budget allocations; you do not need to follow it precisely. Feel free to adjust the percentages to match your needs.

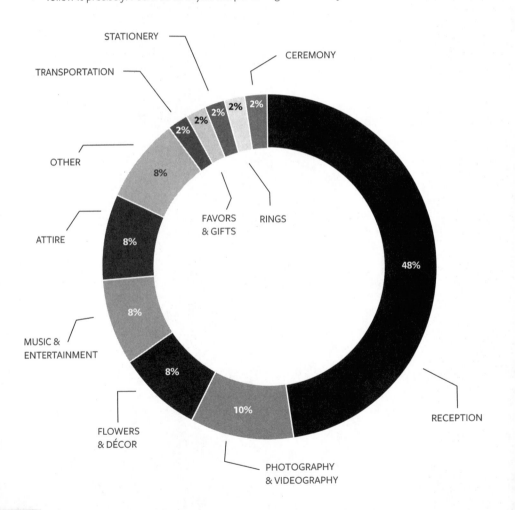

Update your budget every week to make sure you are staying on track. Keep in mind what is most important and what you are willing to sacrifice in order to stay within budget.

What is most important to us?

_____

_____

_____

_____

_____

_____

What area do we least want to spend money on?

_____

_____

_____

_____

_____

What is our budget?

_____

_____

_____

_____

_____

_____

	% Total Budget	Budget Allocation	Amount Spent	Amount Over or Under Budget
Reception	%			
Venue				
Centerpieces				
Seating Chart				
Food & Beverages				
Ceremony	%			
Church Fee				
Church Décor				
Programs				
Photography & Videography	%			
Engagement Photos				
Wedding Photos				
Attire	%			
Wedding Dress & Alterations				
Bride's Accessories				
Tuxedo/Suit				
Groom's Accessories				
Flowers & Décor	%			
Bridal Bouquet				
Centerpieces				
Ceremony Flowers				
Bridesmaids' Bouquets				
Boutonnieres & Corsages				
Flower Girl Petals				

	% Total Budget	Budget Allocation	Amount Spent	Amount Over or Under Budget
Stationery	%			
Stamps				
Save-the-Dates				
Invitations				
Thank-You Notes				
Music/Entertainment	%			
Ceremony Music				
Reception Band or DJ				
Rings	%			
Bride's Wedding Band				
Groom's Wedding Band				
Favors & Gifts	%			
Wedding Favors				
Gifts for Parents				
Gifts for Bridal Party				
Transportation	%			
Wedding Party Shuttle				
Guest Shuttle				
Other	%			
Marriage License				
Post-Wedding Brunch				
Total:				

Selecting Your Support System

Choosing who will help celebrate your special day is an important decision—and not one to rush through. Those who join you at the altar are committing to helping you and your fiancé become the-best-version-of-yourselves and grow together throughout your marriage.

What is most important to you?

....

....

....

....

....

Who are the most significant people in your life?

....

....

....

....

....

Who will best support you in making decisions and managing stress in the planning process?

....

....

....

....

....

....

Who will best support you in your marriage?

_____

_____

_____

_____

_____

_____

OFFICIANTS

If you plan on having a full Mass (see page 36), you will need a priest to officiate and lead the liturgy. If you would like to include more than one, you may invite additional priests to celebrate the Mass alongside the main priest. It is common etiquette to get pastoral approval from the parish priest if you want to have more than one. If your wedding ceremony will not include Mass, you can ask a deacon to officiate.

Priest/Deacon Contact Information

NAME: _____

PHONE: _____

EMAIL: _____

WEDDING PARTY

It is important that your wedding party is a supportive group of individuals you can rely on both during your wedding and in the future. Your best man and maid of honor likely will play a larger role in terms of planning pre-wedding parties and making sure things run smoothly on your big day.

MAID OF HONOR: _____

BEST MAN: _____

BRIDESMAIDS: _____

_____

_____

GROOMSMEN: _____

_____

_____

OTHER ROLES

Depending on whether you are having a full Mass, below are the other roles you can ask loved ones to serve in:

For a ceremony with Mass:

Priest: _____

Ushers: _____

Eucharistic ministers: _____

Readers: _____

Cantors: _____

Altar servers: _____

Gift bearers: _____

For a ceremony without Mass:

Priest or deacon: _____

Ushers: _____

Readers: _____

The Church asks that only baptized Catholics serve as altar servers, readers, and Eucharistic ministers. Be sure to speak with your priest to determine which roles your guests may serve in, as they can provide helpful guidance.

Guests

Celebrating your wedding with family and friends is a wonderful way to say thank you to everyone who has helped you reach this point in your life. These are the people who have helped make you who you are and who will continue to support you in your marriage.

Whether you've imagined a small, intimate wedding or a large wedding, here are a few things to keep in mind as you put together your guest list:

- Budget
- Venue size
- Importance—who absolutely has to be there, and who does not?
- Can people bring guests?
- Can people bring children?
- Are extended family members invited?

To create your guest list, you and your fiancé can each make a list of all of the people you would ideally like to invite. Combine the two lists, count the number of people, and compare it with your venue size and budget. You can then narrow down the list as needed. Finalizing your guest list can be a stressful task. Remember what is most important to you, consider your budget, and work through the list together as a couple.

> **TIP**: After you start receiving RSVPs, you may be able to invite people who did not make the final list. On average, 10 to 20% of your guest list will be unable to attend. Keep a list of other people you would like to invite if enough people decline.

For great resources on preparing for a life together in marriage, visit
DynamicCatholic.com/MarriagePrep

What is most important to you?

Who do you absolutely want to have at your wedding?

What criteria will you use to cut the list if necessary?

Colors

Your wedding colors will be used in invitations, decor, attire, and more. They help set the mood and will be part of mementos for years to come. Work with your fiancé to select your wedding colors. You can keep it simple with 1–2 main colors, or you can select a broader palette.

Here are a few things to consider when picking your colors:

- Keep your colors versatile and complementary, as they will be used in a variety of ways.
- Consider colors that will have flowers in season, and especially remember if there is a particular flower you want to use.
- Different colors look best in different seasons, so keep in mind the time of year you are getting married.
- Look at the colors already in the church and your reception venue.
- Think about the feel you want. For example, more vibrant colors will set a different mood than pastels.

What is most important to you?

....

....

....

....

....

What tone and feel do you each envision?

....

....

....

....

....

NOTES & IDEAS:

Invitations

Depending on your timeline, you may want to send save-the-dates. While this is not necessary, it can be a nice way to share the good news. If you still want to inform guests of the wedding date in advance but have a tighter budget, consider using email or personal social media messages.

Wedding invitations are typically ordered 6–9 months before the wedding and are sent 2–3 months out. These take time to print, address, and mail, so be sure to leave enough time. Consider ordering enough invitations so you have some extras, in case you come across forgotten or last-minute guests you want to invite.

When crafting your invitations, consider your life situation and the level of formality you want. Be sure to include the date, time, and location. It looks more formal if you write out the date and time rather than use numbers.

You can use a professional stationery designer, make your own, or use a printing service to create your wedding invitations. Factors such as the thickness of the cardstock, artwork, and whether you include response postcards for RSVPs will impact the cost and the time it takes for the materials to be ready.

> **TIP**: Instead of including cards for guests' RSVPs, you can save money and time by opting for an online RSVP system, often linked to a wedding website. Be sure to include the website's URL on the invitation.

What do you want in your invitations?

- Main invite with names, date, time, locations
- RSVP card and stamped and addressed return envelope
- Meal card
- Song requests, etc.

What is most important to you?

What tone do you want to communicate?

Do you prefer a more traditional style or something unique?

TO-DO LIST:

☐ **Select photo and/or design for save-the-dates** Due: _____

☐ **Order save-the-dates** Due: _____

☐ **Purchase postage (unless digital)** Due: _____

☐ **Address save-the-dates** Due: _____

☐ **Send save-the-dates** Due: _____

☐ **Select or design invitations** Due: _____

☐ **Order invitations** Due: _____

☐ **Address invitations** Due: _____

☐ **Send invitations** Due: _____

NOTES & IDEAS:

Other Celebrations

It really is a time to celebrate! There often are a variety of parties thrown before and after the wedding. But you do not have to do them all—consider what is most important to you and your fiancé, look at your timeline (and budget, if applicable), and decide how you would like to celebrate.

ENGAGEMENT PARTY

An engagement party can be held shortly after the engagement is announced to celebrate the good news. It is a great opportunity for the bride's and groom's families to meet one another, if they haven't already.

Who hosts: Traditionally the bride's family will host, but it is not uncommon for the groom's family to host.

Who's invited: Close friends and family (customarily, all in attendance will also be invited to the wedding).

LOCATION: _____

DATE & TIME: _____

EMAIL: _____

PHONE: _____

ADDRESS: _____

Notes:

....

....

....

....

....

BRIDAL SHOWER

The bridal shower is typically a women-only luncheon or other midday gathering at a home or restaurant. It often features wedding-themed games and gifts. It is a great opportunity for people to meet the groom, as well, if he would like to come and open presents with the bride.

Who hosts: The mother of the bride or groom or the bridal party. You may have multiple showers if numerous people want to throw you a party.

Who's invited: Female family and friends, as well as the bridal party.

LOCATION: _____

DATE & TIME: _____

EMAIL: _____

PHONE: _____

ADDRESS: _____

Notes:

_____

_____

_____

_____

_____

BACHELOR AND BACHELORETTE PARTY

These parties are an opportunity for the bride or groom and their attendants to spend quality time with one another. It's a great chance to celebrate your upcoming marriage to the person you love. And it's helpful to keep in mind what you hope to experience in these gatherings.

> **TIP**: It is not necessary that the bachelor and bachelorette parties be held the night before the wedding—in fact, it is often better for the bride and groom to have a restful sleep before their wedding. Consider holding these parties at a convenient time before the wedding.

Who hosts: The wedding party (groomsmen for the groom, bridesmaids for the bride).

Who's invited: The wedding party. You may extend the invitation to other family members or friends, if desired.

> **TIP**: Bachelor and bachelorette parties can be as simple as dinner at a nice restaurant, a trip to the movies, wine tasting, a day at the spa, a camping trip, or a round of golf. Your wedding party can help you brainstorm ideas that will create beautiful memories and prepare you to celebrate your big day.

Bachelorette Party

LOCATION: _____

DATE & TIME: _____

EMAIL: _____

PHONE: _____

ADDRESS: _____

Notes:

....

....

....

....

....

Bachelor Party

LOCATION: _____

DATE & TIME: _____

EMAIL: _____

PHONE: _____

ADDRESS: _____

Notes:

....

....

....

....

....

REHEARSAL DINNER

The rehearsal dinner follows the wedding rehearsal, which typically occurs the night before the wedding. At the rehearsal, the celebrants, wedding party, and family run through the ceremony. Afterward, the wedding party and family enjoy dinner together.

Who hosts: Traditionally, the groom's parents will host the rehearsal dinner. However, the bride's parents (or the bride and groom themselves) can host.

Who's invited: The wedding party and immediate family. You may also wish to invite out-of-town guests. While this is not necessary, it is a gesture of appreciation for your guests who have traveled to share your special day with you. If you do choose to include them, make sure they are invited well in advance.

LOCATION: _____

DATE & TIME: _____

EMAIL: _____

PHONE: _____

ADDRESS: _____

Notes:

....

....

....

....

....

POST-WEDDING BRUNCH

A brunch can be held the morning after the wedding at a nearby restaurant or at the hotel where everyone (or a majority of your guests) stayed. It's a way to bid farewell to the newlyweds and provide guests with a meal before they return home.

Who hosts: The groom's parents traditionally host, although the bride's parents may host instead.

Who's invited: The bride, groom, and any wedding guests who stayed overnight.

LOCATION: _____

DATE & TIME: _____

EMAIL: _____

PHONE: _____

ADDRESS: _____

Notes:

_____

_____

_____

_____

_____

What is most important to you?

How do you and your fiancé want to celebrate your engagement?

How do your family and friends want to celebrate your engagement?

The Ceremony

The moment when you say "I do" and give yourself to your spouse is truly special. Inviting God into that moment makes it even greater. Arranging the wedding ceremony is a beautiful part of the wedding planning process.

CHOOSING THE CHURCH

The wedding is typically celebrated in either the bride's or groom's parish. However, it is possible to be married in another parish, with permission on a case-by-case basis. There will likely be a facility fee to help cover basic operation and maintenance costs. Keep in mind that costs will be lower if you are registered parishioners. It also is customary to provide a stipend for celebrants.

DESIGNING THE CEREMONY

The Church offers three forms for the wedding ceremony (called "the Rite of Marriage") to best fit your needs. You will be able to personalize the ceremony by choosing music and selecting from a list of readings and prayers. This is a great opportunity to build a ceremony that is uniquely you and shares your vision and dreams for your marriage.

There are many components to the wedding ceremony, and you will want to familiarize yourself with them in conjunction with your priest or deacon in order to tailor the ceremony in a meaningful way. To help you in making those choices, feel free to make use of the full planning tool, *Planning a Great Wedding Ceremony*, where all of the readings and choices are made available to you.

Before choosing your readings and prayers, you will need to decide which form of the Rite of Marriage to use. Your priest or deacon can help you determine which of the three forms to use.

1. **The Order of Celebrating Matrimony Within Mass**: Also called a Nuptial Mass, this form can be used for two Catholics. It enables the married couple to share the incredible gift of the Eucharist.

2. **The Order of Celebrating Matrimony Without Mass**: This form is used if one of you is a baptized non-Catholic Christian. It is also used if a priest is not available to celebrate the Mass

and a deacon officiates instead. Some couples will elect to use this form if their families or a large number of guests are not Catholic.

3. **The Order of Celebrating Matrimony Between a Catholic and a Catechumen or a Non-Christian**: This form is used when a Catholic marries a catechumen preparing for baptism or an unbaptized person. The couple must receive permission from the local bishop.

For more guidance on planning your wedding ceremony, visit
DynamicCatholic.com/CeremonyPlanner

What is most important to you?

....

....

....

....

....

What do you want to consider when choosing the readings for your ceremony?

....

....

....

....

....

....

What do you hope to share about your dreams for marriage in the ceremony?

....

....

....

....

....

THE GROOM'S ATTIRE

Most grooms choose to wear a tuxedo or a suit, although some opt for a waistcoat or vest for a more casual look. These items, like bridal gowns, come in a variety of styles.

Here is a list of (just a few) things you can customize. It's a good idea to coordinate the groom's accessories with the wedding colors.

- Tie or bowtie
- Boutonniere
- Pocket squares
- Cummerbund
- Cufflinks
- Belt
- Lapel pin
- Suspenders
- Vest
- Jacket or blazer
- Socks
- Shoes

Ideally, the groom will select his tuxedo or suit and get fitted four to five months before the wedding. He can then arrange a pickup date with the shop—usually this is a couple of days before the wedding. As with the bride, it is advisable that he breaks in your shoes before the big day.

> **TIP**: When deciding whether to rent or buy, consider your budget and future needs.

What is most important to you?

How much will the bride's attire influence the groom's?

Do you want the groom to stand out from the groomsmen?

How can you incorporate the wedding colors into the groom's and groomsmen's attire?

NOTES & IDEAS:

- ☐ **Research groom attire** Due: _____

- ☐ **Order groom attire** Due: _____

- ☐ **Choose accessories** Due: _____

- ☐ **Schedule alterations if necessary** Due: _____

- ☐ **Pick up groom attire** Due: _____

THE WEDDING PARTY

Ideally, you will choose and order the bridesmaids dresses 6–9 months before the wedding. A fitting typically is scheduled a few months out.

The groomsmen should be fitted for their tuxedos or suits approximately 4–5 months before the wedding. If they are not able to come to the shop, they can have their measurements taken at any local shop and email them to the tailor.

The color of the bridesmaids dresses typically correlates with the color of the groomsmen's ties, vests, or boutonnieres. Some wedding parties opt for a more creative look, with each member of the party wearing a different style or color.

What is most important to you?

What do you want the wedding party to look like together?

How do you want to incorporate the wedding colors? (Don't forget to think about boutonnieres and bouquets.)

NOTES & IDEAS: BRIDESMAIDS

- ☐ **Research dresses** Due: _____
- ☐ **Get bridesmaids' measurements** Due: _____
- ☐ **Order dresses** Due: _____
- ☐ **Ensure bridesmaids get any necessary alterations** Due: _____

NOTES & IDEAS: GROOMSMEN

TO-DO LIST:

- ☐ **Research groomsmen attire** Due: _____
- ☐ **Order groomsmen attire** Due: _____
- ☐ **Choose accessories** Due: _____
- ☐ **Schedule alterations if necessary** Due: _____
- ☐ **Pick up groomsmen attire** Due: _____

HAIR AND MAKEUP

The bride has several options when it comes to hair and makeup. Play with different hairstyles and see which one works best for you. Try out different shades of eyeshadow, blush, and lipstick.

TIP: Embrace your natural beauty. You want to look authentically yourself when walking down the aisle.

You can hire a professional or a friend to do your hair and makeup, but be sure to do a trial run before the big day. During the trial run, watch what the stylist is doing so you can touch up as needed between the ceremony, photography sessions, and reception.

Brides typically get a haircut 2–4 weeks before the wedding, while grooms go 1–2 weeks out. This ensures that your hair adjusts and has a more natural look.

What is most important to you?

How will you be the most comfortable and confident?

NOTES & IDEAS:

TO-DO LIST:

☐ **Research hair and makeup artists** Due: _____

☐ **Set up trials** Due: _____

☐ **Confirm final details** Due: _____

☐ **Coordinate day-of schedules** Due: _____

☐ **Pay** Due: _____

Hairstylist Contact Information

NAME: _____

PHONE: _____

EMAIL: _____

ADDRESS: _____

WEBSITE: _____

Makeup Artist Contact Information

NAME: _____

PHONE: _____

EMAIL: _____

ADDRESS: _____

WEBSITE: _____

WEDDING BANDS

The wedding bands, a symbol of your union and commitment, play an important role in the ceremony. The rings are blessed and exchanged after vows are recited. Consider ordering your wedding bands and have them fitted by the jeweler 2–3 months before the wedding.

> **TIP**: The engagement ring is typically blessed along with the wedding bands. The bride can choose to wear it as she walks up the aisle and slip it off before the blessing, or it can be kept with the wedding bands.

Notes:

....

....

....

....

....

Flowers & Decorations

FLOWERS

Flowers are a great way to add color to your decor. They are often used for bouquets, corsages and boutonnieres, the ceremony space, and the reception space. If you decide to use a florist, book six to nine months in advance, if possible.

Here are a few things to consider:

- Buying from local shops can save on shipping fees and ensure your flowers arrive undamaged.
- Look for flowers that are in season, as they will be more affordable and easier to obtain.
- You may want to avoid booking your wedding near holidays such as Valentine's Day or Mother's Day, when flower costs skyrocket.
- Many churches have flowers in the sanctuary year-round. If you get married during the last two weeks of Lent, crucifixes and statues in the church may be veiled with purple cloth, or the images may be removed as a form of reflection on the liturgical season. Ask your parish what flowers and decorations will be in the sanctuary based on your wedding date.
- If you would like to preserve the bridal bouquet, have a smaller one reserved for the bouquet toss.

Feel free to use flowers as little or as much as you would like. You can opt to decorate the church pews with ribbon, use candles or mason jars for your centerpieces, or carry a bouquet made from antique brooches. Some couples like to forgo the bouquet and garter toss and wash each other's feet instead, recalling Jesus' actions in John 13. Be creative and find what complements your overall color scheme and style.

> **TIP**: You can spread cheer by donating your centerpieces to nearby retirement homes or hospitals after the wedding!

What is most important to you?

Do you have any particular flowers you like?

Have you seen any bouquet, centerpiece, etc., styles you like?

NOTES & IDEAS:

TO-DO LIST:

☐ **Research florists** Due: _____

☐ **Set up consultation** Due: _____

☐ **Review quote** Due: _____

☐ **Confirm final details** Due: _____

☐ **Coordinate delivery/setup** Due: _____

☐ **Pay** Due: _____

Florist Contact Information

NAME: _____

PHONE: _____

EMAIL: _____

ADDRESS: _____

WEBSITE: _____

Other Decorations

Other decorations for the reception site can be selected from the venue's company, from the caterer, or from a third-party supplier. Select your linens and other decorations when making initial arrangements with the caterer or venue, or shortly thereafter. Depending on your venue, you may need to coordinate delivery and setup.

Some typical decorations to consider include:

- Guest book (or an alternative, such as a piece of artwork you can later hang up in your home)
- Gift table (consider including a box or basket for cards, as many people opt to give money or gift cards at the wedding)
- Place settings (this can include placemats, wedding favors, name cards, menu cards, and dishes, silverware, etc.)
- Centerpieces (these can include flowers, photos, candles, mason jars, table numbers, and more)
- Signage (directional, bar options, menu items, etc.)
- Seating chart so guests know which table to go to (only if you have assigned seating)
- Memorial to loved ones who have passed away (this can be as simple as a sign saying "In memory of" with names listed and a candle lit)
- Photo booth (some couples opt to purchase simple props and encourage the use of a hashtag or set up a tablet with a photo booth app)

What is most important to you?

What do the church and reception already offer?

NOTES & IDEAS:

Photography & Videography

PHOTOGRAPHY

Photographs of your special day will be treasured for years to come. When choosing the person to capture these precious moments, consider the following:

- What is the photographer's experience?
- Do you like their style?
- How much does it cost?
- How much of the day comes with each package? (8 hours, full day, etc.)
- What prints, digital files, albums, or other packages do they offer?

You likely will need to book your photographer 6–9 months before the wedding.

TIP: If you want engagement photographs, you may be able to save money by using the same photographer for both occasions. The engagement photo shoot is also a great time to test how your bridal makeup looks in photographs.

You may want to prepare a list of moments you would like your photographer to capture, such as the bride getting ready, the groom's reaction to seeing her walk down the aisle, and the first dance. You can also submit a list of group photos you would like taken, such as the wedding party and family portraits.

☐ **Research photographers** Due: _____

☐ **Set up consultation** Due: _____

☐ **Review quote** Due: _____

☐ **Schedule engagement photos** Due: _____

☐ **Confirm final details** Due: _____

☐ **Pay** Due: _____

Photographer Contact Information

NAME: _____

PHONE: _____

EMAIL: _____

ADDRESS: _____

WEBSITE: _____

VIDEOGRAPHY

Some couples also hire a videographer. Book yours six to nine months out. If you decide to use a videographer, watch sample footage to ensure you like their style.

Your videographer can be creative, capturing interviews from guests and "exclusive sneak peeks" throughout the day. Be sure to discuss what you would like when booking your videographer, and ask about costs for various packages they offer.

What is most important to you?

....

....

....

....

....

What do you want to capture in photos and/or video?

....

....

....

....

....

Are there any particular moments that are important to you?

....

....

....

....

....

Are your photographer and videographer familiar with Catholic weddings?

....

....

....

....

....

NOTES & IDEAS:

TO-DO LIST:

☐ **Research videographers** Due: _____

☐ **Set up consultation** Due: _____

☐ **Review quote** Due: _____

☐ **Confirm final details** Due: _____

☐ **Pay** Due: _____

Videographer Contact Information

NAME: _____

PHONE: _____

EMAIL: _____

ADDRESS: _____

WEBSITE: _____

Looking for more wisdom on the wedding day? Visit **DynamicCatholic.com/Marriage**

Wedding Website and Registries

Many couples create a wedding website with helpful information, photos of the happy couple, and stories (how they met, the proposal, etc.). Your website can also include the ability to RSVP, event locations and times, maps, hotel accommodations, and fun things to do in the area.

Perhaps one of the biggest benefits of creating a website is the ability to link it to your gift registries, which makes shopping for wedding gifts easy for your guests.

You ideally will want to start building your registries 6–9 months before the wedding. You can always add more items as you get closer to the wedding date.

Most couples register with 2–3 stores. Consider including both online and brick-and-mortar options. Also consider offering a variety of price points, as some guests will be able to afford more expensive gifts than others.

> **TIP**: Be aware of the stores' exchange and return policies before you register with them, as you may receive duplicate gifts.

Establish what items are most essential, and be mindful of the size of your first home and how much storage space you will have available. If you prefer to save up for something special, you can set up a digital cash registry that allows guests to give money rather than gifts. Be aware that online cash registries may charge a transaction fee.

What is most important to you?

What do you already have?

What is your current lifestyle?

How will your lifestyle change in the next five years?

NOTES & IDEAS:

Transportation

The day of the wedding will be chaotic, so it is helpful to plan in advance how you will get to the wedding, reception, and hotel. Some people opt for a limousine, while others simply coordinate rides with the wedding party.

You may also want to consider providing transportation via buses or vans for guests from the church to the reception site. Contact transportation and rental companies 4–5 months before the wedding.

What is most important to you?

_____

_____

_____

_____

_____

What is the distance between locations (getting ready, church, reception, hotel)?

_____

_____

_____

_____

_____

NOTES & IDEAS:

Gift Etiquette

If guests are invited to multiple pre-wedding parties, each guest is generally only expected to provide one gift. For example, if the mother of the bride and mother of the groom each host a bridal shower, the bridesmaids are only expected to present the bride with a gift at one of these gatherings. They will likely still want to get you a wedding gift, but communicate to them that you do not expect gifts at every party.

> **TIP**: Keep track of the gifts you open and who they are from. This will make writing thank-you cards easier down the road.

GIFTS FOR THE WEDDING PARTY

It is customary to give your wedding attendants a gift prior to the wedding. The groom gets a gift for each of his groomsmen, and the bride gets a gift for each of her bridesmaids. This is a great way to thank them for being a part of your big day.

> **TIP**: If you want your bridesmaids to wear matching jewelry on the day of the wedding, you can buy them a necklace or earrings as their gift. Or, you could treat them to a manicure and/or pedicure so they have matching nail polish.

GIFTS FOR EACH OTHER

The bride and groom may want to exchange gifts with each other as well. It can be as simple as a letter, a handkerchief, a list of reasons you love him or her, or a bottle of wine to open on your one-year anniversary.

GIFTS FOR YOUR PARENTS

It is customary for the bride and groom to give their parents a gift to show their appreciation. It does not have to be elaborate. It can be as simple as a montage of family photos, a hand-stitched message on the father's tie, or a beautiful bracelet for the mother.

GIFTS FOR GUESTS

Wedding favors provide your guests with keepsakes to remember your special day. Common wedding favors include personalized keychains, bottle stoppers, or coasters.

TIP: Consider giving your guests more meaningful wedding favors. Some couples will give handmade rosaries or a copy of a beloved book. Instead of purchasing wedding favors, some couples donate to a favorite charity and provide guests with cards stating a donation was made in their name.

What is most important to you?

....
....
....
....
....
....

What do you want to communicate with your gifts?

....
....
....
....
....
....

NOTES & IDEAS:

Reception

The largest portion of the budget is typically spent on the reception. It will help you immensely to keep in mind what is most important to you and your fiancé, what you hope to accomplish, and what budget you want to maintain. You will want to book your reception venue 10–12 months out.

It is helpful to consider the following when booking your reception site:

- Availability
- Capacity
- Price
- Distance to church and hotel
- Additional fees
- What's included?
- Are you required to work with certain vendors?
- Do you have access prior to the reception to set up?

SETUP

If the venue is not responsible for setting up the reception, make sure you have people available to help and a checklist of what needs to be done. Work with your wedding coordinator or day-of coordinator, if you have one, to secure the details. Be sure to know when materials should be dropped off at the site and how much time you will have to set up.

Consider the following when arranging for setup:

- Room layout (tables, bar, dance floor, gift table, photo booth, DJ or band, etc.)
- Centerpieces and place settings
- Sweetheart table or head table for the wedding party
- Signage (directing your guests to the reception, seating charts, etc.)

What is most important to you?

_____

_____

_____

_____

_____

How do you want to interact with your guests throughout the night?

_____

_____

_____

_____

_____

NOTES & IDEAS:

FOOD

When choosing your catering, ask yourself: Do we want a full meal or simple cocktails and hors d'oeuvres? Do we want a buffet, sit-down, or family-style meal? What menu options would we like to offer?

> **TIP**: There likely will be details specific to your reception that differ from vendors' typical routines. You will want to be explicitly clear with each vendor on your expectations at and before the reception.

Hors d'oeuvres are traditionally served if you are providing a cocktail hour directly after the ceremony. This is a great time for you to get some photographs taken.

Your caterer likely will have a variety of options and price points for meals. More exotic dishes will increase the price per plate, while simpler items will be less expensive. If budget is a concern, ask your caterer about cost-effective alternatives. If any of your guests have dietary restrictions or food allergies, communicate this clearly with your caterer ahead of time.

> **TIP**: You can consider options other than working with traditional caterers. Consider fun and creative alternatives like your favorite restaurant, Mexican, BBQ, etc. This can bring a unique and enjoyable vibe, while also lowering costs.

It is customary to feed all wedding professionals (photographer, videographer, DJ or band, etc.). Your caterer may provide discounted costs for these meals.

What is most important to you?

Do you want to consider any alternative options?

BEVERAGES

Beverages can be a major expense. Depending on your budget, you may want to provide an open bar, which means you pay for your guests do drink unlimited quantities. Alternately, you may want to simply offer beer, wine, and a few signature drinks. Or, you can have a cash bar, in which guests pay for their own drinks. Be sure your caterer or beverage provider has a liquor license.

If you will be serving alcohol at your wedding, talk with your caterer about their corkage fees. It may be more cost effective to purchase your own alcohol. You should budget for one drink per person, per hour.

Consider offering non-alcoholic options such as soda, punch, tonic water, coffee, and tea as well.

What is most important to you?

Do you want to include any special beverages?

DESSERT

While most bridal magazines showcase beautiful, multi-tiered cakes with detailed piping and elegant columns, you have a variety of options when it comes to serving your guests dessert and can get creative. You could have a sundae bar, cookies, or even s'mores.

Order any desserts at least 2–3 months before the wedding. Attend a tasting and select the flavors and decorations you would like. Communicate with your baker how many guests will be in attendance. Be aware that many bakers have setup and delivery fees, and arrange setup times well in advance.

> **TIP**: Your caterer may also have contracts with local dessert providers and may be able to offer discounted rates if you book through them.

If you are serving cake, you likely will need to purchase a cake knife. If you use a third-party bakery, the reception site or caterer may charge a cake-cutting fee. However, if you order your cake through them, this fee may be waived.

What is most important to you?

Do you want to consider any alternative options?

NOTES & IDEAS:

☐ **Research caterers** Due: _____

☐ **Set up tastings** Due: _____

☐ **Review quotes** Due: _____

☐ **Select caterer** Due: _____

☐ **Confirm final details** Due: _____

☐ **Pay** Due: _____

Caterer Contact information

NAME: _____

PHONE: _____

EMAIL: _____

ADDRESS: _____

WEBSITE: _____

MUSIC

One of the things wedding guests often look forward to is dancing at the reception. You have several options when choosing your reception music. Some couples create their own playlist on a tablet and plug it into a speaker, while others hire a DJ or live band. What you choose to do will depend on your personal taste and budget, and what you hope to accomplish with your reception.

A band member or DJ may also serve as the emcee throughout the reception. Be sure to give them a list of the information necessary (such as names) well in advance.

What is most important to you?

What kind of atmosphere do you want to set with the music?

Band or DJ Contact Information

NAME: _____

PHONE: _____

EMAIL: _____

ADDRESS: _____

WEBSITE: _____

NOTES & IDEAS:

SCHEDULE

Below is a list of details that you will need to coordinate for the reception. Remember—this is your party, and you get to make it your own. Add, remove, or substitute whatever works best for you, and fill out the timeline on the next page with your schedule.

- The caterer, venue, or designated team sets up the reception and ensures food, signage, and decorations are in place
- Guests arrive, sign the guestbook, and find their tables (if seating is assigned)
- Cocktails and hors d'oeuvres are served while the wedding party and family have pictures taken
- The emcee welcomes the wedding party and announces the bride and groom
- The best man and maid of honor toast the bride and groom
- The bride and groom share their first dance
- The bride and her father share a dance
- The groom and his mother share a dance
- The father of the bride or other family member briefly welcomes everyone
- The priest or a family member offers a prayer before dinner
- Dinner is served
- The dance floor is opened
- Cake is cut and distributed
- Bouquet toss, foot washing, etc.
- Dancing continues
- The bride and groom exit
- The caterer, venue, or designated team takes down all decorations and equipment

Time	Event

Legal Checklist

As churches cooperate with state regulations, your marriage must be validated by the state. Requirements will vary by state, so consider researching your state's requirements at least 2–3 months before the wedding to ensure there are no surprises.

MARRIAGE LICENSE AND CERTIFICATE

You likely will have to submit an application prior to the wedding. The application may or may not have a fee, and may include a blood test or proof of vaccination.

You can plan to retrieve the license approximately one month before the big day. Your priest or officiant will sign it after the wedding and send it to the county office. As soon as the license is processed, you will be mailed a marriage certificate.

CHANGE OF NAME AND ADDRESS

You will need to notify several parties of any change of name and address. Below are a few places to contact after you have your marriage certificate:

- ☐ Social security office
- ☐ Department of Motor Vehicles
- ☐ Employers
- ☐ Banks and credit card companies
- ☐ Insurance companies
- ☐ Mortgage or leasing agencies
- ☐ Post Office
- ☐ Internal Revenue Service
- ☐ Voter registration office
- ☐ Telephone companies
- ☐ Utility companies
- ☐ Bureau of Consular Affairs (if you have a passport)
- ☐ Car title office
- ☐ Attorneys
- ☐ Doctors' offices

Inspiration for the Journey

Your journey together is just beginning! And it will be beautiful.

As you challenge and encourage each other to become the-best-version-of-yourselves, Dynamic Catholic wants to be a resource for you. Visit **dynamiccatholic.com/Growth** to find inspiring books, videos, articles, events, and more to help you grow personally and as a couple.

To get the full Dynamic Catholic marriage preparation experience and explore Better Together, visit **dynamiccatholic.com/WeddingPrep**. The videos, inventory, and more will help you build a great marriage.

May God bless you and your marriage!

For more wisdom on a lifelong, life-giving marriage, visit **DynamicCatholic.com/Marriage**

Notes:

Notes:

Notes: